UPBEAT!

For Piano

Alison Bowditch

CONTENTS

Level 2

First published 1997
by Subject Publications
Beech House
Broadstone
Dorset BH18 9NJ
Tel: 01202-696907
Fax:01202-657743

ISBN 1 898771 05 7

★ ★ ★ ★ ★ ★

Acknowledgements

From the sale of this book the Composer and Publishers will make a donation to The Beethoven Fund For Deaf Children (Charity Registration no. 282844).

★ ★ ★ ★ ★ ★

Printed by Pardy & Son (Printers) Ltd.,
Parkside, Ringwood, Hampshire BH24 3SF
Tel: 01425 471433
Fax: 01425 478923

For Tom

★ ★ ★ ★ ★ ★

ABOUT THE COMPOSER

Alison Bowditch obtained at Cardiff University the prestigious Bachelor of Music honours degree with musical composition as a principal specialisation. She studied piano under Richard McMahon and oboe under John Williams. She embarked upon a teaching career after completing the one-year post-graduate certificate course at Rolle College, Exmouth.

Alison teaches a wide range of woodwind instruments, as well as piano and voice, to pupils of all ages. She successfully combines her work as a composer with her rôle as a mother of three young children. In addition to composing for the Playing Is Fun series, Alison finds time to play in a county orchestra and to fulfil professional engagements as a musician in her own right.

★ ★ ★ ★ ★ ★

FOREWORD

The Playing Is Fun series aims to capture your imagination and increase your enjoyment of music. Whatever your age, you will find these original compositions for piano or keyboard both exciting and inspiring. Among the many and varied rhythmical styles are those of jazz, swing, rock, blues and boogie.

Each piece is a challenge and an adventure with its own mood and rhythm for you to discover. To help you with each interpretation, the composer has suggested a suitable tempo and style; she has also indicated possible fingering wherever appropriate. As you progress, you will meet a widening range of key signatures, time signatures and rhythm patterns.

At every level, Upbeat for Piano by Alison Bowditch is great fun to hear and play.

Maureen Cox

Groovin'

With a strong pulse. ♩ = 120. (♪♪ = ♩♪ triplet)

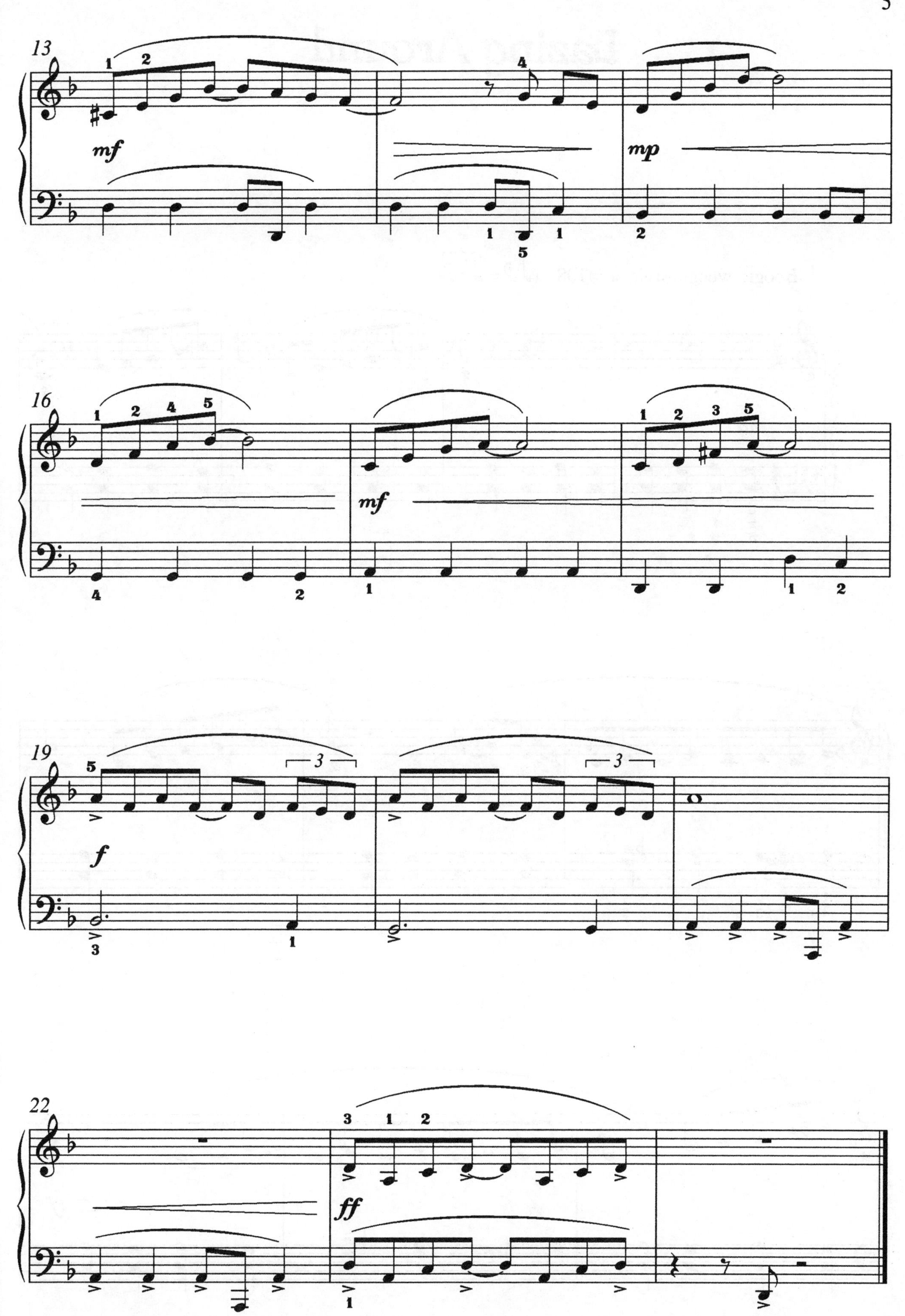
mf
mp
mf
f
ff

Lazing Around

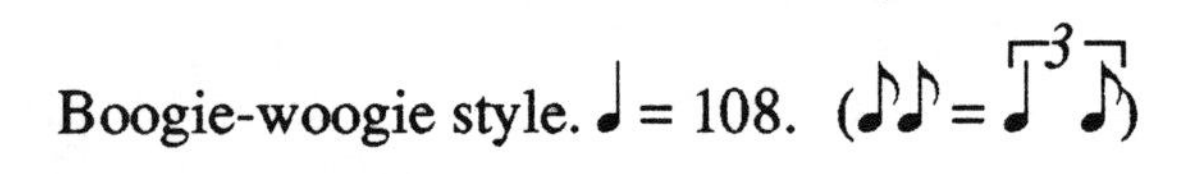

11
3
3
3
3
3
3
2
3
mp
1
4
2
5

14
3
3
mf

17

20
rit.
mp
1
4
2
4
2
4
2
1
2
1
5

Moonrise

With mystery and atmosphere. ♩ = 108.

18
RH
22
rit.
a tempo
mp
f
26
mf
RH
mp
30
rit.
a tempo
p
33
rall.
p

Mock-Bach-Rock

1.
2.
mf
f
rall.
mp

The Stately Stegosaurus

Fine
More movement. ♩ = 96
D.S. al Fine

Stage-Struck

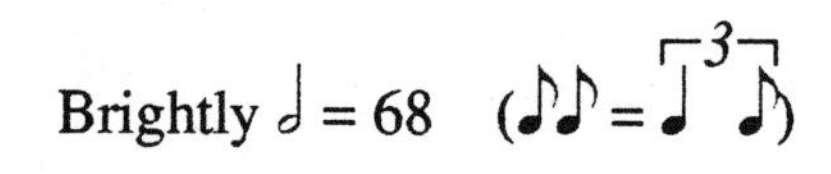

13

16
f
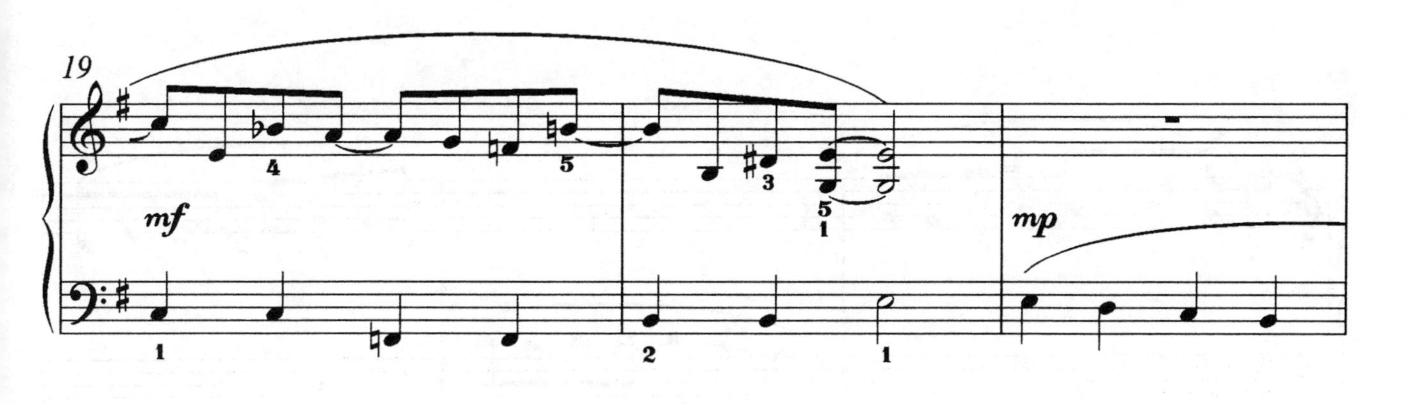
19
mf
mp
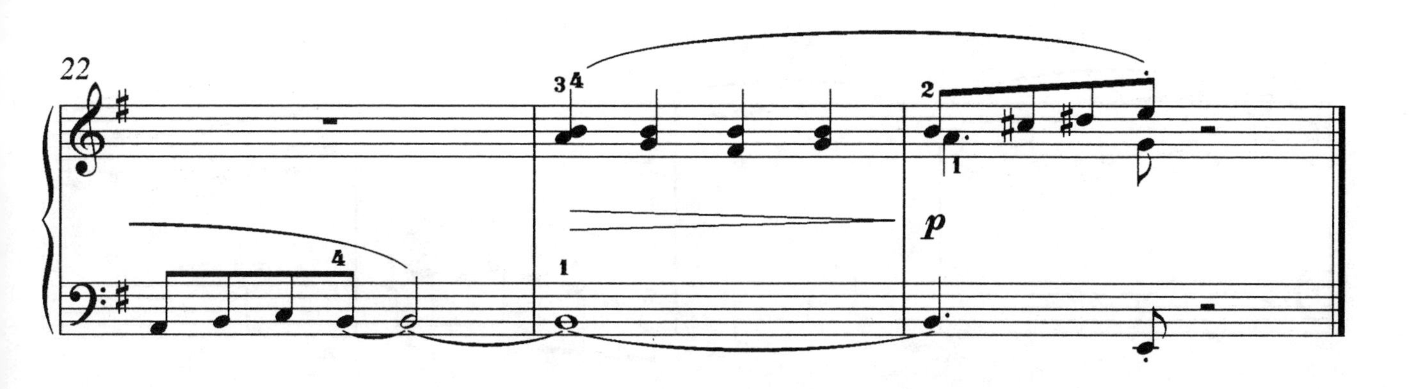
22
p

The Dreamer

Very smoothly. ♩ = 116.

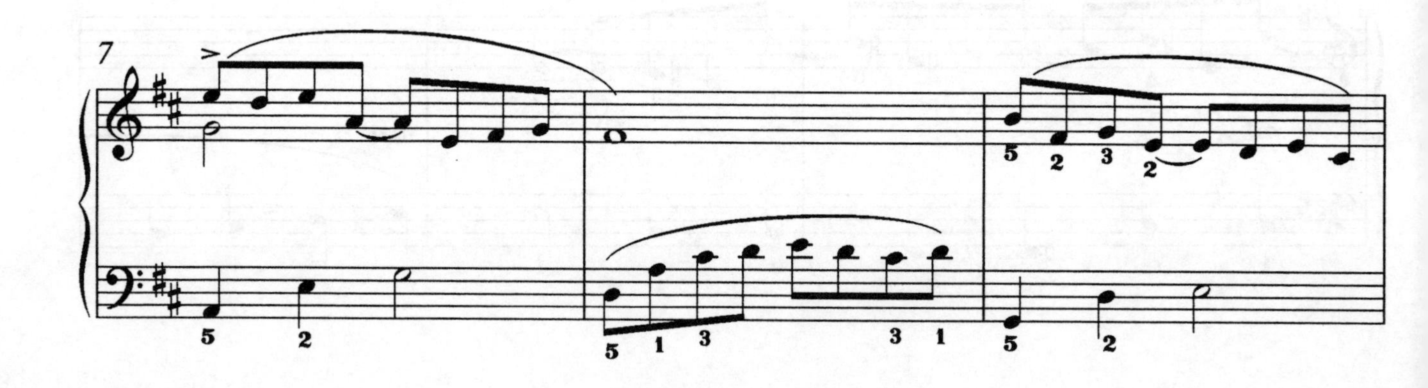

14
cresc.

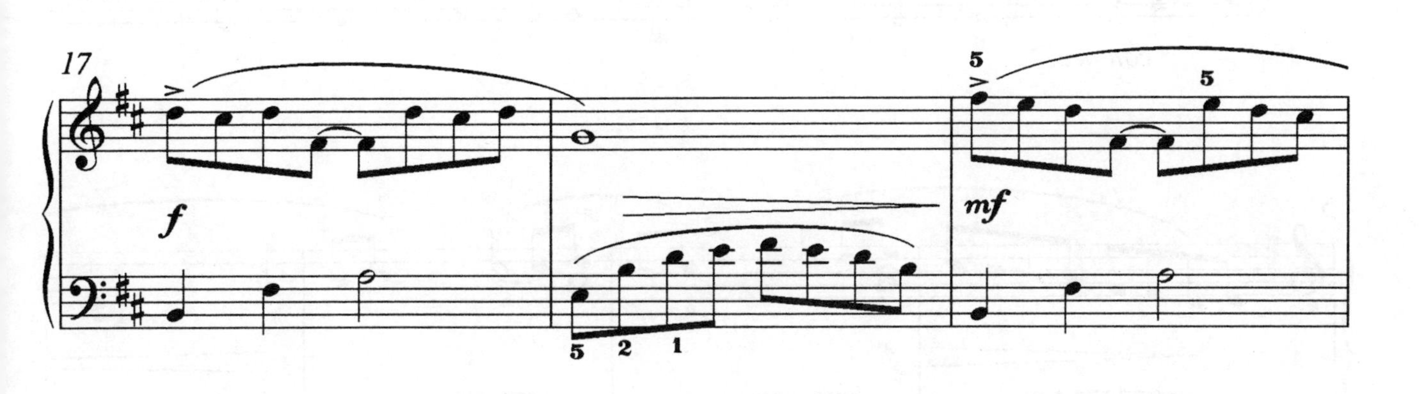
17
f
mf

20

23
rit.
p

Caribbean Cocktail

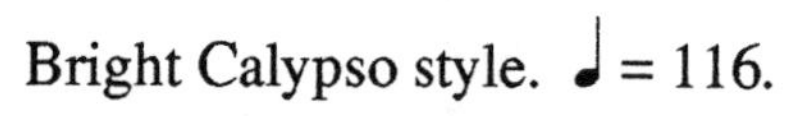

f
mf
p (echo)
mf

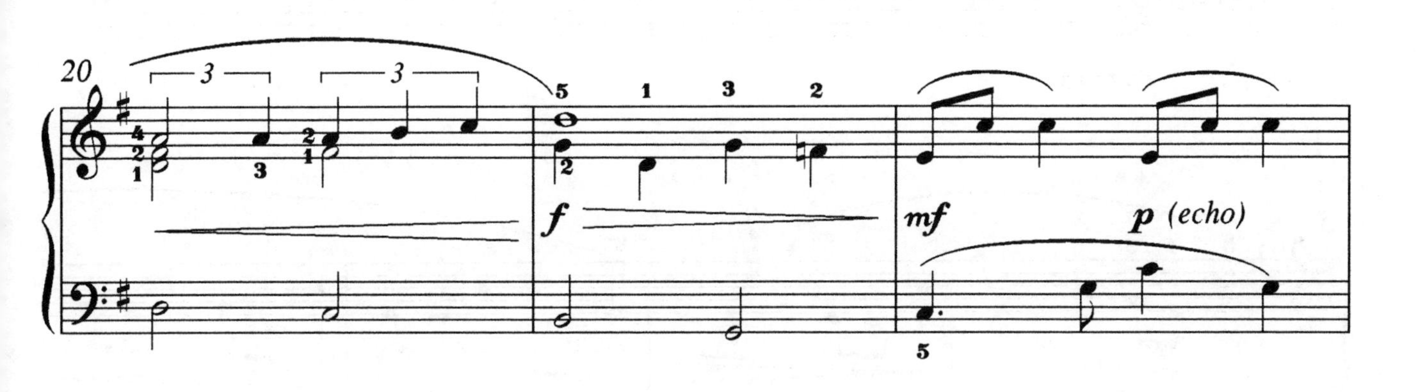
f
mf
p (echo)

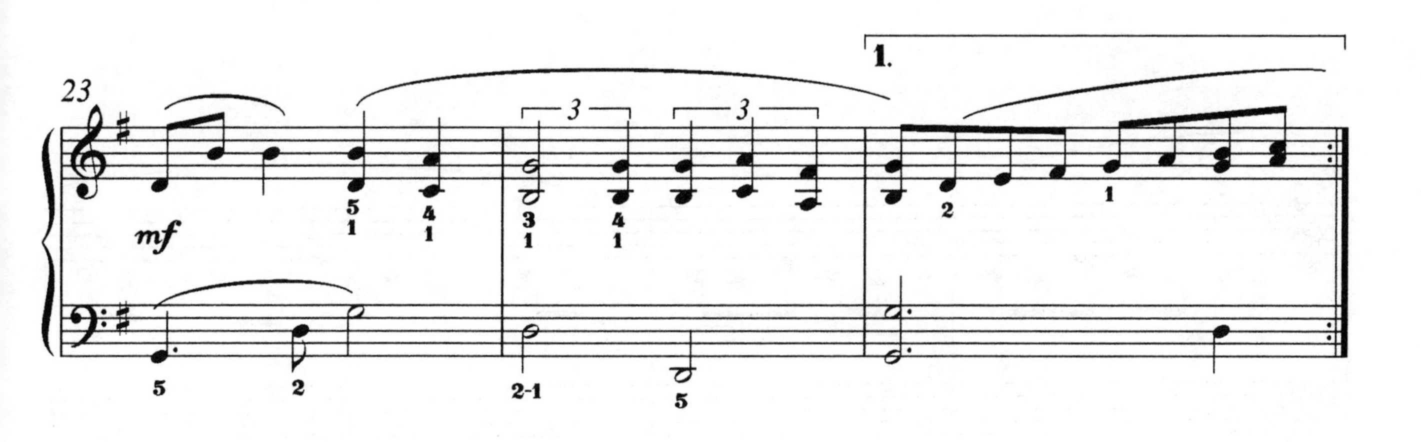
mf

f
mf

Drifting

Flowing and gentle. ♩. = 72.

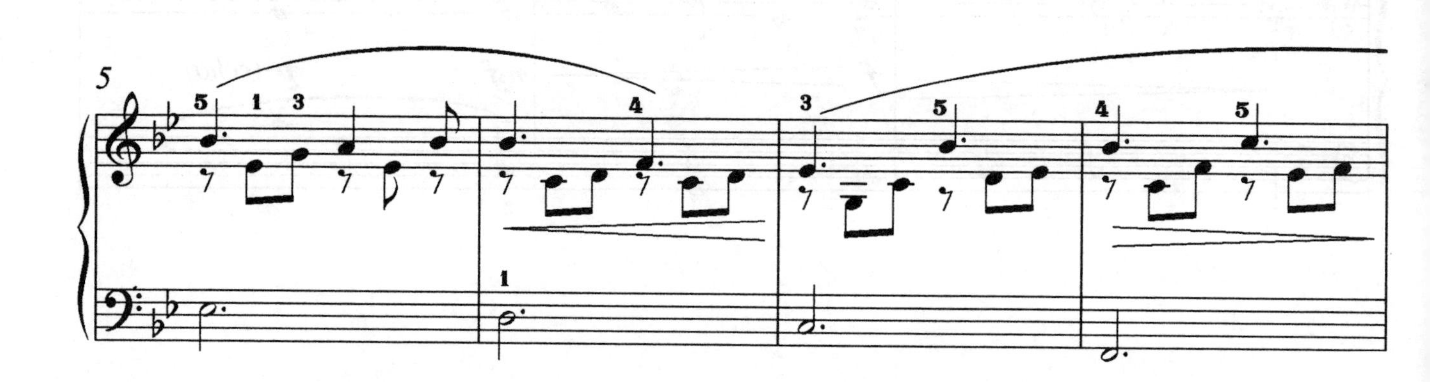

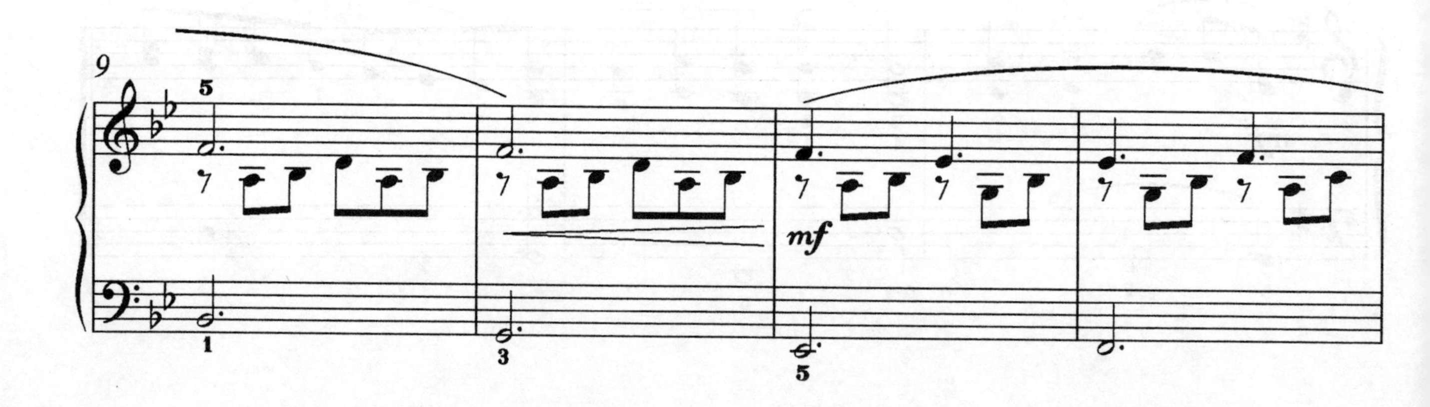

17
21
mf
p
26
31
mf
35
decresc.
pp

Stay Cool

With vitality. ♩ = 132.

mf

ff

Ped.

13
mf
subito p
mf
3

16
subito p
mf
subito p
3

19
mf
subito p
mf
3
Ped.

22
rall.
ff
mf
3
Ped.

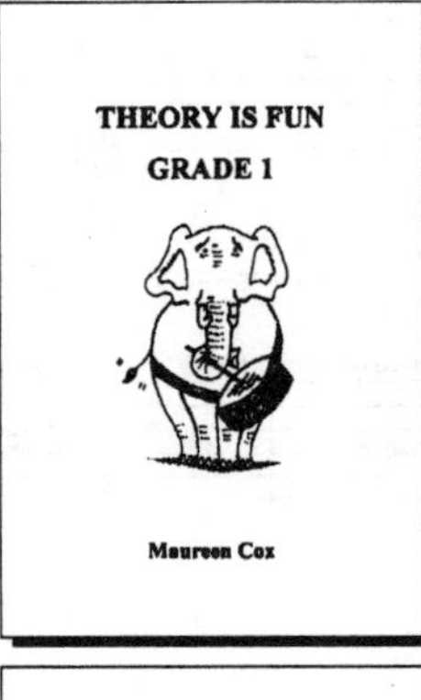

Treble clef, bass clef, notes and letter names. Time names and values; dotted notes, tied notes and rests.
Accidentals. Tones and semitones.
Key signatures and scales (C, G, D & F Major).
Degrees of the scale, intervals and tonic triads.
Simple time signatures and bar-lines.
Writing music and answering rhythms.
Musical terms dictionary and list of signs.

ISBN 0-9516940-8-1

Major key signatures and scales to 3 sharps or 3 flats.
A, D and E minor key signatures and scales.
Degrees of the scale and intervals. Tonic triads and accidentals.
Piano keyboard, tones and semitones.
Simple time signatures. Grouping notes and rests. Triplets.
Two ledger lines below and above the staves.
Writing four-bar rhythms
More musical terms and signs.

ISBN 1-898771-02-2

Major and minor key signatures to 4 sharps or 4 flats.
Harmonic and melodic minor scales.
Degrees of the scale, intervals and tonic triads.
Simple and compound time signatures. Grouping notes and rests. Transposition at the octave.
More than two ledger lines.
Writing four-bar rhythms. Anacrusis. Phrases.
More musical terms and signs.

ISBN 1-898771-00-6

All key signatures to 5 sharps or 5 flats. Alto clef; chromatic scale, double sharps and flats. Technical names of notes in the diatonic scale. Simple and compound time: duple, triple, quadruple. Primary triads: tonic, subdominant and dominant.
All diatonic intervals up to an octave. Recognising ornaments.
Four-bar rhythms and rhythms to words.
Families of orchestral instruments and their clefs.
More musical terms, including French.

ISBN 1-898771-01-4

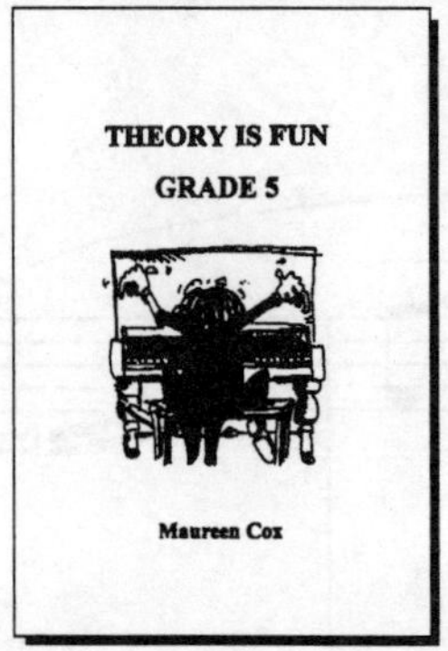

All key signatures to 7 sharps or 7 flats. Tenor clef and scales.
Compound intervals: major, minor, perfect, diminished and augmented. Irregular time signatures: quintuple and septuple.
Tonic, supertonic, subdominant and dominant chords.
Writing at concert pitch. Short and open score. Orchestral instruments in detail. Composing a melody for instrument or voice. Perfect, imperfect and plagal cadences.
More musical terms, including German.

ISBN 0-9516940-9-X